The Adventures of Nairobi Raine is a book series that tells the story about the adventures of a precocious and curious baby named Nairobi. Her friend, Mr. All Knowing, takes her on numerous adventures to teach her about the world and the people in it. Through these explorations she gets to meet and see the beauty of life that awaits her.

The initial book series will consist of the following parts:

MEETING MR. ALL KNOWING
NAIROBI VISITS MR. RAIN
NAIROBI VISITS MS. SUNSHINE
THE LAND OF LAUGHTER
THE VALLEY OF TEARS
and more.

Nairobi Raine was living in her mommy's tummy for only eight months when she decided that she wanted to get out and see the world and meet people that her mom cooed to her about each day.

She could not wait to see the happy smiling faces of her parents and feel their arms around her, or meet her aunts and uncles, and her grandmother who was getting ready to move to somewhere called Barbados.

Nairobi could hear the voices of all the people who couldn't wait to meet her and who loved her.

Although she did not know what love meant, she was sure that it was a good thing because she felt warm and tingly inside whenever the word was mentioned, and this put her in a calm and sleepy mood.

Nairobi's mom started to lull her to sleep by singing her favorite song. Nairobi mimics the words as her mother sings.

You are my sunshine
My only sunshine
You make me happy
When skies are gray
You'll always know dear how much I love you
Please don't take my sunshine away.

As the song ends, Nairobi sleepily wonders what sunshine is. Was it warm and wet like her comfortable bed? Was it soothing like her mummy's voice or her daddy's laughter, or comforting like the thought of meeting the people in her village that her parents always talked about?

Hmm thought Nairobi, how am I ever going to find out what this sunshine is like? I know wha I will do. I will ask my friend Mr. All Knowing.

With that, Nairobi, wide awake, sets off on her merry way to find her friend Mr. All Knowing, for as his name suggests Mr. All Knowing knows everything that there is to know.

After a bit of searching, Nairobi happened upon Mr. All Knowing sitting and reading his book and laughing out loud.

"Good morning Mr. All Knowing," said Nairobi, "I have been looking up down and all around to find you."

"Hi there little one!" shouted Mr. All Knowing followed by a deep booming laugh. "How can I help you now that you have found me?"

"Well Mr. All Knowing my mom is always singing to me about sunshine and I would just like to know what it is like." At this question, a beautiful smile, followed by a strange look spread across Mr. All Knowing's face.

"Why do you have that look on your face Mr. All Knowing?" asked Nairobi. "Is sunshine a terrible thing?" "No little one," he replies, "sunshine is beautiful. It is warm and bright like a beautiful smile."

"So why did you frown?" asked Nairobi. "Since you are now saying that sunshine is a beautiful thing. I really do not understand any of this Mr. All Knowing. Your reaction seems a bit confusing."

"Well Nairobi dear, that is because as I was thinking of Sunshine or Ms. Sunshine. I was also thinking of her opposite Mr. Rain."

"Ms. Sunshine is a person? Why does one person remind you of the other Mr. All Knowing?" asked Nairobi. "Are they family? Do they belong to the same village?"

"Well, they are opposites my dear," said Mr. All Knowing. "But I feel that in order for you to appreciate Ms. Sunshine, I should introduce you to Mr. Rain first." So off went Nairobi and Mr. All Knowing to meet Mr. Rain.

About the Author

Andrea Belmar, the author of The Adventures of Nairobi Raine, is a child at heart, and enjoys being able to write through the eyes of a child.

She was born in Barbados and emigrated to the United States as a teenager. Andrea's love for reading started at an early age when she realized that with the help of her imagination, she could become anyone, do anything, or go anywhere just by sticking her nose in a book.

She always wanted to pass on to other children the wonders of reading that she experienced as a child and so her passion for writing children's books only increased with time.

At the tender age of 52, with her very supportive family cheering her on, she decided to go after her dreams and wrote her first book.

Andrea was always curious about the belief that a child can hear while in the womb, so when her sister became pregnant with her niece, Andrea's imagination took off, and that is when the Adventures of Nairobi Raine was born.

When Andrea is not transporting young minds to exciting places where they meet interesting people and learn new things, she can be found traveling, reading, writing poems or songs, and most importantly playing dress up with her niece.

Published by Judy's Child, LLC

CPSIA information can be obtained
at www.ICGtesting.com
Printed in the USA
BVHW060046110821
614090BV00015B/992